Inventor's Notebook

these notes belong to

Archie Drury

part of **Mega Makers!** at

© Scripture Union 2013
First published 2013
ISBN 978 1 84427 788 9

Scripture Union
207–209 Queensway
Bletchley
Milton Keynes
MK2 2EB
email: info@scriptureunion.org.uk
www.scriptureunion.org.uk

The right of Ro Willoughby to be identified as the author of this work has been asserted by them in accordance with the Copyright, Designs and Patents Act 1988.

Scripture quotations are from the Contemporary English Version published by HarperCollinsPublishers © 1991, 1992, 1995 American Bible Society or from the Good News Bible, published by The Bible Societies/ HarperCollins Publishers Ltd, UK, © American Bible Society, 1966, 1971, 1976, 1992. Used by permission.

British Library Cataloguing-in-Publication Data

A catalogue record of this book is available from the British Library.

Printed and bound in India by Nutech Print Services India

Cover and internal design by kwgraphicdesign

Cover illustration by Sean Parkes

Internal illustration by Sean Parkes

Scripture Union is an international Christian charity working with churches in more than 130 countries.

Thank you for purchasing this book. Any profits from this book support SU in England and Wales to bring the good news of Jesus Christ to children, young people and families and to enable them to meet God through the Bible and prayer.

Find out more about our work and how you can get involved at:
www.scriptureunion.org.uk (England and Wales)
www.suscotland.org.uk (Scotland)
www.suni.co.uk (Northern Ireland)
www.scriptureunion.org (USA)
www.su.org.au (Australia)

Copies of the CEV Bible can be purchased from: www.bibleresources.org.uk

Inventor's Notebook

In these pages, you will find out more about Jesus' love for you. The more you get to know him, the bigger and bigger you discover his love is for you. Jesus' followers found this out as they travelled with Jesus.

You will join them on their journey as you read for yourself the stories in the Bible that you have been hearing at **Mega Makers!** Plus... DID YOU KNOW? facts pages, puzzles, talk with God suggestions, space for you to record your own thoughts and lots more.

The Bible is split into two sections (the Old Testament and the New Testament). These two sections are split into books (the Old Testament has 39 books and the New Testament has 27). The books are split into chapters and those chapters are split into verses. Sometimes you'll see a Bible verse written like this: **Matthew 8:26**. Here is how you tell which verse to read:

Matthew means we need to look for the Bible book of Matthew. If you are not sure where that is look for the contents page near the beginning of the Bible.

Matthew **8** : **26**

26 means we need to look for the little number 26; we call it verse 26.

8 means we need to look for the big number 8; we call it chapter 8.

INVENTOR'S MEGA CODE BREAKER!

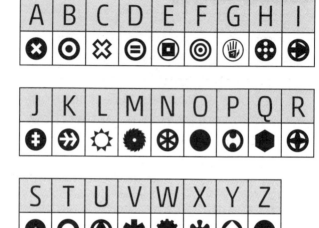

Paul, one of the first people to travel around Europe telling people about Jesus, wrote to the Christians who lived in Ephesus to remind them to be strong in their faith. He wanted them to know how wide, how long, how high and how deep Jesus Christ's love was for them. Here is what he wrote in code. It is the Learn and remember verse for **Mega Makers!**

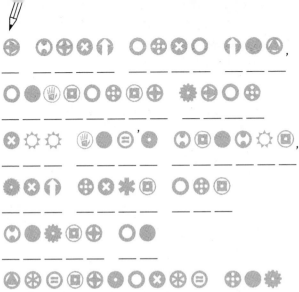

Ephesians 3:18 (GNB)

MEGA INVENTIONS

At **Mega Makers!** we will watch the launch of the Mega Machine, which amazingly enlarges a small object into something much bigger! It is a picture of how the more we discover about God's love for us, the bigger and bigger we discover his love is. Wow!

As you will have guessed, the machine does not really enlarge things. It is an imaginary invention. But God's inventions are real. After all, he created the whole world. As human beings we are like God in that we also invent things. From the beginning of time mankind has invented different tools, ways of cooking, ways of living and so much more.

Use the codebreaker on page 4 to work out the names of six things that have been invented in the last 10 years.

What other modern inventions can you think of? Who invented them?

....

....

....

....

2001

__ __ __ __

2002

__ __ __ __ __   __ __ __ __ __   __ __ __ __

2003

__ __ __ __ __ __ __   __ __ __ __ __

(battery-operated for underwater use!)

2005

__ __ __ __ __ __ __

2007

__ __ __ __ __ __

2007

__ __ __   __ __ __ __ __ __

(with an LED light to wake you gently!)

Wider & wider
THE INVITATION TO FOLLOW JESUS

Jesus chose twelve men to travel with him to share their lives together. These were his close friends. One of these friends was Matthew, also known as Levi. Matthew collected taxes for the Romans from people who traded food, tools, building materials, wood, cloth, goats, sheep, wine – that sort of thing. This made Matthew unpopular. Few people liked anyone who worked for the Romans, let alone a taxman. Even today people grumble about 'the taxman' who they think will take lots of money off them!

Read Matthew 9:9 below and then, on the next page, draw where you think Matthew was sitting when Jesus walked by. What do you think might have happened to the money he collected when he left it to follow Jesus?

How many extra coins can you find hidden in the table?

Matthew 9:9
⁹ As Jesus was leaving, he saw a tax collector named Matthew sitting at the place for paying taxes. Jesus said to him, "Come with me." Matthew got up and went with him.

DID YOU KNOW?

🔹 The coins Jesus used were Roman, Greek, Syrian and Jewish.

🔹 Large amounts of money were in talents and minas.

🔹 Silver coins were the Syrian stater, and the Roman denarius or the Greek drachma (both worth less than half the stater). A man got paid one denarius for a day's work.

🔹 The bronze Jewish shekel was worth the same as the stater. (Jews were only allowed to issue bronze coins.)

🔹 Roman taxes were paid in denarii. That was what Matthew collected.

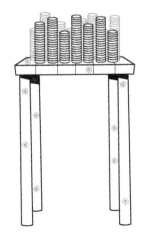

Jesus also invited all sorts of other people to follow him, to listen to him, to be like him. These were often people who were unpopular or not respectable.

Read about Matthew's dinner.

Matthew 9:10–13

[10] Later, Jesus and his disciples were having dinner at Matthew's house. Many tax collectors and other sinners were also there. [11] Some Pharisees asked Jesus' disciples, "Why does your teacher eat with tax collectors and other sinners?"

[12] Jesus heard them and answered, "Healthy people don't need a doctor, but sick people do. [13] ... I didn't come to invite good people to be my followers. I came to invite sinners."

Draw two of Matthew's guests, one of Jesus' close friends and Jesus around the table opposite. Draw one Pharisee on the grey cross, standing looking superior. (The Pharisees were the religious leaders and they had nothing to do with 'sinners'.)

What could Jesus have meant when he said he was like a doctor? Put these words of Jesus in verse 12 into your own words.

"Healthy people don't need a doctor, but sick people do. I didn't come to invite good people to be my followers. I came to invite sinners."

If you had been in Matthew's house at this meal, where would you be in the room? Sitting with Jesus and Matthew's friends or standing in the corner with the Pharisee?

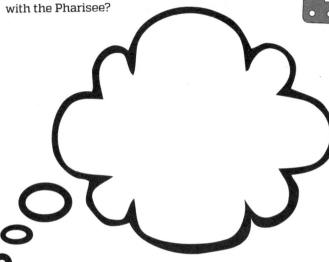

Jesus' invitation to people to follow him spread **wider and wider**. But not everyone wanted to accept. Some people thought they were good enough and did not want to be called a 'sinner'. They didn't think they needed Jesus to help them live in a way that pleases God. But Matthew's friends wanted to please God and they wanted to learn from Jesus. That's why they were only too happy to sit down and have a meal with him.

Write down the name of each member of your Toolshed. You could draw a little picture of them. Count how many in the group can be described by the word below each cog. Put the number in the centre of the cog.

....

....

....

....

....

....

....

....

NO GLASSES

GLASSES

SHORT HAIR

WEARS GREEN

WEARS PINK

GIRLS

HAS A BROTHER

NOT AT MY SCHOOL

LONG HAIR

AT MY SCHOOL

HAS A SISTER

BOYS

We are all so different from each other. Can you think of other ways you are different from members of your Toolshed?

....

....

....

God has made us to be different from each other. Jesus invites each one of us to follow him, whatever we are like. That invitation includes you. At **Mega Makers!** you will discover more about his love for us.

Talk out loud to Jesus and say:

Thank you, Jesus, that I am different from

.... (the person sitting next to you)

because ....

Thank you, Jesus, that you love them. Amen

Deeper&deeper

THE TRUST IN JESUS

Jesus and his followers would not forget this boat trip. Their feelings changed so much.

Decide which of these six expressions best fits how his followers felt.

1 Happy

2 Tired

3 Wet

4 Frightened

5 Shocked

6 Safe

Write the number of the feeling in the empty box beside each sentence or phrase.

Matthew 8:23-27

23 After Jesus left in a boat with his disciples, ☐

24 a terrible storm suddenly struck the lake, and waves started splashing into their boat. ☐

Jesus was sound asleep, ☐

25 so the disciples went over to him and woke him up. They said, "Lord, save us! We're going to drown!" ☐

26 But Jesus replied, "Why are you so afraid? You surely don't have much faith." Then he got up and ordered the wind and the waves to calm down. And everything was calm. ☐

27 The men in the boat were amazed and said, "Who is this? Even the wind and the waves obey him." ☐

DAY 2

At what point in Matthew's story do you think Jesus' feelings were different from those of his friends?

....

....

....

DID YOU KNOW?

- The deepest point in the earth's oceans is the Challenger Deep in the **Mariana Trench** in the North Pacific Ocean. It is 10,924 meters (35,840 feet) below sea level. If Mount Everest, the highest mountain on Earth, was placed on the sea bottom at this point it would be covered by over one mile of water. It is named after the British survey ship Challenger II, which discovered this in 1951.

- The **Congo River** is the deepest river in the world measuring 230 meters (755 feet) in the deepest trench.

- The **River Thames** is the deepest river in Great Britain. Its depth varies according to the time of year, the amount of rainfall and the tide but at its deepest it is 25 metres.

- The deepest oil well in the world is 12,376 metres deep and is in the **Chayvo oil field** on the Sakhalin shelf in the Russian Far East.

- It is now assumed that the **Yarlung Tsangpo**, near the Tibet-India border is the deepest canyon in the world, measuring 6,000 metres deep.

> How often do you say that something is deep?

How could Jesus sleep while the furious storm was raging?

The disciples had already seen Jesus do some amazing things by healing lots of people.

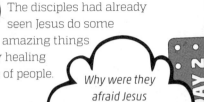

Why were they afraid Jesus would not keep them safe?

Jesus' disciples discovered four things about what it means to be a follower of Jesus.

✱ They followed Jesus into the boat. **Being a follower means DOING what Jesus does, being like him**.

✱ They got on with their ordinary jobs as fisherman and Jesus went to sleep. **Being a follower means KNOWING Jesus is with us when we do ordinary things.**

✱ They got into trouble and panicked, so they woke Jesus up. **Being a follower means ASKING Jesus to help when things are difficult.**

✱ They were amazed at what Jesus did. **Being a follower means being amazed by Jesus and PRAISING him.**

Because of what they saw Jesus do, their trust in him just got deeper and deeper.

When have you needed to trust Jesus? How can your trust in Jesus get deeper and deeper?

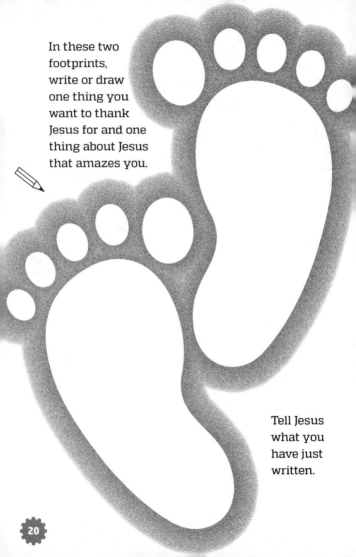

In these two footprints, write or draw one thing you want to thank Jesus for and one thing about Jesus that amazes you.

Tell Jesus what you have just written.

How many differences can you spot
in these 'before and after' pictures?

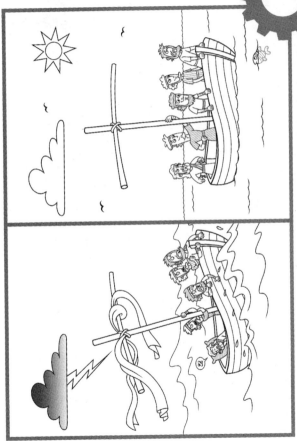

Stronger & stronger

THE POWER OF JESUS

When we talk about someone or something 'being strong' we mean different things.

For example, pushing or lifting something heavy, or being brave, or having powerful muscles, or being someone other people lean on for help, or doing something amazingly difficult, or a powerful storm.

Write on the dotted line, who is being strong at each step in Matthew's story in Matthew 9 verses 18 to 26?

Matthew 9:18

[18] While Jesus was still speaking, an official came and knelt in front of him. The man said, "My daughter has just now died! Please come and place your hand on her. Then she will live again."

Psst:
Many people who went to Jewish synagogues did not like what Jesus said and did. They certainly would not have gone to ask Jesus for help.

Step 1: ....

Psst:
Did Jesus or the leader know what was going to happen at the house? On the way, a woman in the crowd touched Jesus wanting him to heal her – and Jesus did. The writers Mark and Luke wrote that as soon as the woman touched Jesus he felt power leave him. She bravely spoke up and admitted she had touched him.

Matthew 9:19,23a

[19] Jesus and his disciples got up and ... [23] ... went into the home of the official.

Step 2: ....
....

DAY 3

Matthew 9:23–24

When Jesus went into the home of the official and saw the musicians and the crowd of mourners, [24] he said, "Get out of here! The little girl isn't dead. She is just asleep." Everyone started laughing at Jesus.

Psst:
As soon as someone died, professional musical mourners came to make loud wailing sounds. As it was a hot country, the funeral took place soon afterwards. These musicians did not think Jesus could do anything.

Step 3: ....

Psst:

Everyone was amazed. They all knew the girl was truly dead! They must have asked, "What sort of power does Jesus have to bring this girl back to life? Who is he?"

Matthew 9:25-26

²⁵ But after the crowd had been sent out of the house, Jesus went to the girl's bedside. He took her by the hand and helped her up.

²⁶ News about this spread all over that part of the country.

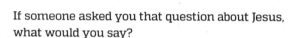

Step 4:

If someone asked you that question about Jesus, what would you say?

Help Jesus and the father find their way back to the house where the girl has died.

What did Jesus' followers discover about Jesus in this story?

If you were feeling weak, afraid or alone, what sort of powerful person would you want with you?

If you can't do something, or just don't understand, what sort of powerful person would you want with you?

Can you tell the story in your own words?

DID YOU KNOW?

⚙ **The scarily strongest man in the Bible** is the Philistine giant, Goliath. His bronze chest armour alone weighed 57kg! But his strength did not protect him from David, the shepherd boy, who killed Goliath with a stone catapulted into his forehead. David shouted out to Goliath, "I've come out to fight you in the name of the LORD All-Powerful... Then the whole world will know... The LORD always wins his battles, and he will help us defeat you." (I Samuel 17:45,47)

⚙ **The most powerful kings in the Bible** are King David and his son, King Solomon. David won the most battles and in their combined years as kings they ruled over the most people and the most land. But after their reigns, the kingdom of God's people was divided into two. Their power did not last.

⚙ **The most powerful person in the Bible** is Jesus. He did not look like a powerful person. He was born in an ordinary family. He died a horrible death as a criminal. But he gave clues that he was God himself by the way he performed miracles and by what he said. The biggest clue was that he came alive again from the dead and 40 days later went back to heaven. This is God's power at work. The more we know about God, the **stronger and stronger** we realise his power is.

There are lots of hands in this story. The leader pleads with Jesus, the woman in the crowd touches Jesus, Jesus shoos away the musicians and Jesus takes the girl by the hand. Just as the father held out his hands to ask Jesus to come, we can ask Jesus to help us.

Write or draw on this hand something you want to ask Jesus for.

A pet dog white dog called Fluta right now or m should now.

When we pray we place ourselves in the powerful hands of Jesus. His power will make a difference.

How well do you know the Learn and remember verse from Ephesians 3:18? Fill in the gaps and, only when you have finished, look up page 5 to check the missing words.

I p_ _ _ that you, t_ _ _ _ _ _ _ _ _ with

all God's p_ _ _ _ _ _ , may have the power to

u_ _ _ _ _ _ _ _ _ _ _ _ how b_ _ _ _ _

and l_ _ _ _ , how h_ _ _ _ and d_ _ _ _ , is

C_ _ _ _ _ _ _ '_ l_ _ _ _ .

What have you discovered so far about Jesus' love and power?

....

....

....

....

....

Greater&greater

Here is part of the story of Jesus' arrest and how he was put to death. It comes from Matthew chapters 26 and 27.

Read the story and, using these different lines, underline the words written about these groups of people:

* **Religious leaders**: a zigzag line
* **Soldiers**: a line of arrows
* **The crowd of people**: a dotted line
* **Followers of Jesus**: a line of kisses
* **Jesus himself**: a line of tiny crowns

Matthew 26:36–41,50,56

36 Jesus went with his disciples to a place called Gethsemane. When they got there, he told them, "Sit here while I go over there and pray." 37 Jesus took along Peter and the two brothers, James and John. He was very sad and troubled, 38 and he said to them, "I am so sad that I feel as if I am dying. Stay here and keep awake with me."

39 Jesus walked on a little way. Then he knelt with his face to the ground and prayed, "My Father, if it is possible, don't make me suffer by having me drink from this cup. But do what you want, and not what I want."

[40] He came back and found his disciples sleeping. So he said to Peter, "Can't any of you stay awake with me for just one hour?[41] Stay awake and pray that you won't be tested. You want to do what is right, but you are weak."

[50] Jesus replied, "My friend, why are you here?"

The men grabbed Jesus and arrested him.

[56] ... all of Jesus' disciples left him and ran away.

Matthew 27:27–46,50,54

[27] The governor's soldiers led Jesus into the fortress and brought together the rest of the troops. [28] They stripped off Jesus' clothes and put a scarlet robe on him. [29] They made a crown out of thorn branches and placed it on his head, and they put a stick in his right hand. The soldiers knelt down and pretended to worship him. They made fun of him and shouted, "Hey, you king of the Jews!" [30] Then they spit on him. They took the stick from him and beat him on the head with it.

[31] When the soldiers had finished making fun of Jesus, they took off the robe. They put his own clothes back on him and led him off to be nailed to a cross. [32] On the way they met a man from Cyrene named Simon, and they forced him to carry Jesus' cross.

[33] They came to a place named Golgotha, which means "Place of a Skull." [34] There they gave Jesus some wine mixed with a drug to ease the pain. But when Jesus tasted what it was, he refused to drink it.

[35] The soldiers nailed Jesus to a cross and gambled to see who would get his clothes. [36] Then they sat down to guard him. [37] Above his head they put a sign that told why he was nailed there. It read, "This is Jesus, the King of the Jews." [38] The soldiers also nailed two criminals on crosses, one to the right of Jesus and the other to his left.

[39] People who passed by said terrible things about Jesus. They shook their heads and [40] shouted, "So you're the one who claimed you could tear down the temple and build it again in three days! If you are God's Son, save yourself and come down from the cross!"

[41] The chief priests, the leaders, and the teachers of the Law of Moses also made fun of Jesus. They said, [42] "He saved others, but he can't save himself. If he is the king of Israel, he should come down from the cross! Then we will believe him. [43] He trusted God, so let God save him, if he wants to. He even said he was God's Son." [44] The two criminals also said cruel things to Jesus.

[45] At noon the sky turned dark and stayed that way until three o'clock. [46] Then about that time Jesus shouted, "Eli, Eli, lema sabachthani?" which means, "My God, my God, why have you deserted me?"

[50] Once again Jesus shouted, and then he died.

[54] The officer and the soldiers guarding Jesus ...saw everything that happened. They were frightened and said, "This man really was God's Son!"

| SOLDIERS | THE CROWD | JESUS' FOLLOWERS | JESUS |

Tick which of these people you feel sorry for?

Put a cross beside which of these people could have done something different. Think what they might have done instead.

Look at the first part of the story you have just read. What else do you think Jesus could have done?

....

....

....

....

....

Jesus did not have to die but chose to die because that was what God his Father wanted him to do. So we do not need to feel sorry for Jesus. He was doing what pleased God. The more we discover about Jesus, the **greater and greater** we understand his love.

MEGA WORDSEARCH

The names of most of the people in the story of Jesus' death you have just read are in this wordsearch. Can you find them?

R	O	B	B	E	R	S	F
E	R	E	C	I	F	F	O
L	E	A	D	E	R	S	L
I	L	P	E	T	E	R	L
G	P	T	H	J	I	J	O
I	O	E	A	O	D	A	W
O	E	B	R	H	L	M	E
U	P	L	M	N	O	E	R
S	A	M	Y	E	S	S	S

The spare letters complete this statement.

Jesus took ___ ___ ___   ___ ___ ___ ___ ___ for all the wrong things we have ever said, done or thought.

(That is why we do not need to feel sorry for Jesus but be thankful that his love for us was so great.)

Write or draw something you want to say to
Jesus about his love.

Here are some
suggestions and
you can use more
than one of them:

DAY 4

⚙ Thank him that he loves you so much
to take the blame for the wrong you
have done.

⚙ Draw or write the name of someone
who needs to know Jesus loves them.

⚙ Draw a big smile because it makes
you happy to know Jesus loves you.

⚙ Draw a sad mouth because you
know you have done things which
displease God.

⚙ Draw a question mark because you
are thoughtful and want to find out
more.

⚙ Just write a message to Jesus.

Jesus said, "The greatest way to show love for friends is to die for them." (John 15:13) Jesus himself did far more than that because he died for those who were his enemies. By doing this, he made it possible for everyone to become his friends. What is more, we know that he died on the Friday but came alive again on the Sunday. His death was not the end of him.

What can you do today to show that you love someone else? God is not asking you to die for someone but to serve them in some way, which may mean doing something difficult. Write or draw what ideas you have.

DAY 4

For **ever** & **ever**

FRIENDSHIP WITH JESUS

Jesus was buried in a cave before it got dark on the Friday. His friends and followers all went home because Saturday was their day of rest. The religious leaders put their own soldiers to guard the tomb and rolled a great stone over the entrance. They did not want anyone to steal Jesus' body.

Read what happened early on the Sunday morning.

Matthew 28:1-10

[1] The Sabbath was over, and it was almost daybreak (*dawn*) on Sunday when Mary Magdalene and the other Mary went to see the tomb. [2] Suddenly a strong earthquake struck, and the Lord's angel came down from heaven. He rolled away the stone and sat on it. [3] The angel looked

as bright as lightning, and his clothes were white as snow. ⁴ The guards shook from fear and fell down, as though they were dead.

⁵ The angel said to the women, "Don't be afraid! I know you are looking for Jesus, who was nailed to a cross. ⁶ He isn't here! God has raised him to life, just as Jesus said he would. Come, see the place where his body was lying. ⁷ Now hurry! Tell his disciples that he has been raised to life (*risen*) and is on his way to Galilee. Go there, and you will see him. That is what I came to tell you."

⁸ The women were frightened and yet very happy, as they hurried from the tomb and ran to tell his disciples.

⁹ Suddenly Jesus met them and greeted them. They went near him, held on to his feet, and worshiped him. ¹⁰ Then Jesus said, "Don't be afraid! Tell my followers to go to Galilee. They will see me there."

DAY 5

WHAT DID JESUS SAY?

From the clues below and the Bible story on pages 38 and 39, fill the grid opposite and discover in the shaded vertical boxes what Jesus first said when he met the women!

1   Who came down from heaven
2   The name of the two women.
3   What the soldiers shook with.
4 and 9   The angel's clothes were _____ as _____
5   The women clung onto Jesus' _____
6   Jesus had _____ from the dead.
7   The time of day the women came to the tomb.
8   The angel and Jesus told the women to ____ and tell.

Think about

If you had been there with the women, think of one word to describe what you would have felt when:

✸ they arrived at the tomb and saw the soldier guarding the entrance?
....

✸ the angel came down?
....

the soldiers fell flat on the ground?
....

the angel started speaking to them?
....

they met Jesus?
....

The women were very afraid but very happy all at the same time. They soon discovered that Jesus was going to be their friend for ever and ever. They had such good news to tell Jesus' followers and probably everyone they knew. Jesus was alive!

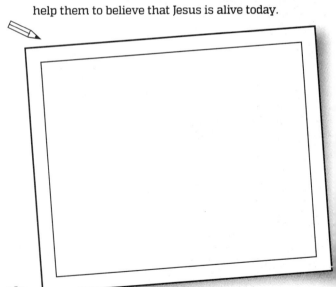

Draw in the picture frame someone you know who you could tell about Mega Makers! You can tell them that Jesus is alive. Then pray that God will help them to believe that Jesus is alive today.

Jesus kept his promise and he met with his followers in Galilee. A bit later he went up a mountain with them. Soon after that he returned to heaven to be with God his Father. He sent the Holy Spirit to come in his place. Unlike Jesus, the Holy Spirit can be everywhere all at the same time.

You can read this story in Matthew chapter 28 verses 16 to 20. Use the code to work out what Jesus said to his followers.

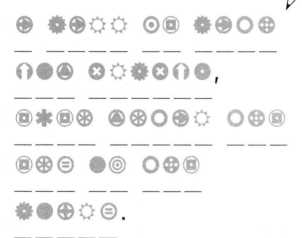

DAY 5

BECOMING A FOLLOWER OF JESUS

All through **Mega Makers!**, you have been finding out what it means to be a follower of Jesus. Circle what is the closest to what you now think about Jesus.

I like what I've heard about Jesus. I would like to know more.

There is lots I don't understand and I need someone to help me find out more.

I am not really bothered about following Jesus.

I'm already a follower of Jesus and have learnt lots more about him at **Mega Makers!**

I've been impressed by Jesus' love for his followers and how he inspired them to follow him.

Chat to your Toolshed leader about what you have circled. They would love to know and can help you, if that's what you want.

We don't need special words to talk with Jesus. We can talk with him just as we talk with a friend. Jesus wants us to love and follow him. Remember what his followers discovered about following Jesus when they were in the boat in the storm.

Look back to page 19.

But the wrong things we do often make us feel awkward. We've let him down. We find it impossible to be like him. Jesus wants to forgive us for all the wrong we have done. That's why he died, to take the blame for all the wrong anyone has ever done. Once we've asked Jesus to forgive us, he gives us his Spirit (the Holy Spirit) who helps us live like him. Then we can talk with him without feeling bad.

You can ask Jesus to forgive you in your own words. But if you are not sure what to say, you could use this prayer.

Lord Jesus, I want to follow you and be your friend.

Thank you that you came to earth to show us how much God loves us.

Thank you that you died on the cross to take the blame for all the wrong things I have ever said, or done, or thought.

Please forgive me so that I can follow you and be your friend...and may the Holy Spirit help me be more like you.

Amen.

My best bits!

The **funniest** bit:

when joker said
blintce biirk dmmii yon
tines.

The **silliest** bit:

when ftt ftn said tund
tuna batman.

The bit I wanted to go on **longer**:

46

What I **learnt** about Jesus:

What I will **remember** most:

What I will **tell my friends** at school about:

Memories of the Toolshed

Collect the names, messages and doodles of everyone else in your Toolshed group.